# Phonicability

**COLLETTE DRIFTE**

**RECEPTION**

HOPSCOTCH PUBLISHING

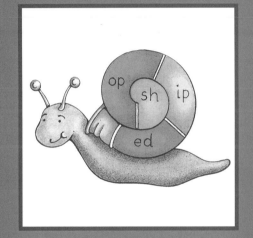

_ouse

jump under

ca_

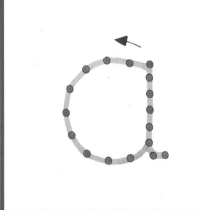

# Phonicability

## CONTENTS

Published by Hopscotch Educational Publishing Ltd,
29 Waterloo Place, Leamington Spa CV32 5LA

© 2000 Hopscotch Educational Publishing

Written by Collette Drifte
Series design by Blade Communications
Illustrated by Susan Hutchison
Cover illustration by Susan Hutchison
Printed by Clintplan, Southam

ISBN 1-902239-50-4

# Introduction

## ABOUT THE SERIES

'Throughout Key Stage 1, phonics should be the main focus of the 15-minute word level slot in the Literacy Hour.' This is the directive to be found in *Phonics, Progression in phonics: materials for whole-class teaching* issued by the DfEE in 1999. Such an emphasis being placed on the teaching of phonics illustrates its importance.

*Phonicability* is a series of books which provides individual worksheets that support and consolidate the teaching of phonics skills as outlined in the *National Literacy Strategy Framework for Teaching*. There is one book for each year of Key Stage 1 (Scottish Primary 1–3): *Reception* (Scottish Primary 1), *Year 1* (Scottish Primary 2) and *Year 2* (Scottish Primary 3).

A unique feature of the series is the provision of differentiated photocopiable activity sheets aimed at considerably reducing teacher-preparation time. These sheets present the same activity at three different levels, for below average, average and above average children. They are also differentiated across the year of work, thereby reflecting the expected progress of the child. The worksheets tie in closely with the term-by-term teaching of phonics as detailed in the *National Literacy Framework*. While they leave the teacher free to approach phonics lessons in the most appropriate way for each particular class, they provide a useful extra source of practice material to reinforce and consolidate the teaching points. It is vital that an adult reads the sheets with the children first before expecting them to start work.

Children as young as those at Key Stage 1, who are learning formal literacy and phonics rules for the first time, need a great deal of repetition, practice and consolidation. The provision of as much varied material as possible is essential. Teachers can never have too many ideas and materials for this purpose!

The contents of the books for Year 1 (Primary 2) and Year 2 (Primary 3) follow a similar format; this is useful for classes with mixed ages.

At the back of each book is a Record/Assessment Sheet. This details the goals for each year, as outlined in the *National Literacy Framework*, and provides a useful record of what the child has achieved, what they need to consolidate and what their next targets should be.

## ABOUT THIS BOOK

This book is for teachers of Reception year (YR) children (Primary 1). It aims to:

○ provide differentiated material which will support and consolidate the phonics rules taught during the Literacy Hour
○ provide extension activities that can be worked on independently both during the Literacy Hour and at other (unstructured) times in the day
○ provide repetition and practice of the current rule being taught, while simultaneously reinforcing other aspects of work at word level in the *National Literacy Framework*
○ enable the children to work independently, thus allowing the teacher to work with other groups or individual children simultaneously.

## THE PHOTOCOPIABLE ACTIVITY SHEETS

The differentiated sheets introduce the same phonics rule and have the same task, but at three different ability levels. They also provide a variety of activities to consolidate the same teaching point. They are designed to stimulate the children's thinking and to keep up their interest level. The format is not identical on every sheet and so the child will not suffer from 'worksheet fatigue'; boredom is guaranteed to kill motivation!

The activities on each sheet introduce the phonics rule being taught, but they also introduce and use the vocabulary of the *National Literacy Framework*, such as 'sentence', 'word', 'write' and 'draw'. While these are not among the high frequency words to be taught at Reception age, nevertheless they are words that the children need to become accustomed to hearing and using appropriately. There is a bonus also in seeing them in written form.

Some of the sheets, particularly the earlier ones, include drawing activities. These fulfil several purposes. Correct pencil grip (tripod) can be established and maintained, hand-eye coordination will be practised and spatial awareness will be developed. Drawing style and ability, sometimes a marker to difficulties the child may be experiencing, also become apparent through these activities. An observant teacher can quickly detect any problems in these areas and remedy them early on.

The order of the activity sheets is not a recommendation to teach the sounds in the same order. They have been presented in the book to follow alphabetical order and the digraph order as outlined in the *National Literacy Framework* documents. It is suggested that the teacher should read *Phonics, Progression in phonics: materials for whole-class teaching* (DfEE, 1999) and follow its suggestions for teaching order and technique. Teaching points in the suggested activities are in line with the document's recommendations. For example, the correct technical terms are adopted (such as 'phoneme' instead of 'sound'), as are the preferred pronunciations (such as 'ssss' instead of 'suh').

## THE EXTENSION ACTIVITIES

The sheets also offer extension activities. These can be done on the back of the sheet and should be done independently, thus eliminating the need for adult supervision, although help with reading the instructions will be needed. The extension activities are designed to reinforce the work done on the main sheet and provide extra practice in the rule being taught.

At the end of each section there are also sheets which have activities incorporating a mixture of the teaching points. These offer an extra opportunity for consolidation, and also allow the teacher to ensure that a concept has been firmly grasped.

## ASSESSMENT

The sheets themselves build up to provide a portfolio of the child's work and progress. This is a useful resource for assessment and recording, particularly if evidence is needed at a later stage of the child's development. It is suggested that the sheets are kept in a folder or binder. A busy classroom teacher can easily lose sight of how a child performed at the beginning of the year. The sheets will provide evidence of the child's development.

## THE ALIEN CHARACTER

Throughout the book (and indeed the series), a space character is used to introduce each phonics rule and to assist the children with the individual activities on the worksheet. The alien in this book is Zep, whose name comprises a consonant-vowel-consonant.

When a classroom session reaches the point of using the activity sheets, introduce Zep to the children and read the instructions on each sheet with them. Children of Reception age have expressive and receptive language skills far in advance of their reading and writing ability. While not necessarily being able to read the instructions at this stage, they will easily understand the instructions on the sheets if they are read out to them.

## CHAPTER CONTENT

**Overall aims**
This outlines the aims for the section content.

**Teacher's notes**
This provides information and suggestions regarding the content of the section.

**Intended learning**
This states the specific learning goals for the activities.

**Suggested activities**
This offers suggestions for activities which enable the children to practise, consolidate and reinforce the phoneme being taught. The activities are there for the teacher to pick and choose from according to the class/group needs. They are suggestions only, and as such can be adapted and altered in any way to suit the specific needs of each situation. They are varied in their nature, involving both physical and intellectual abilities.

**Using the differentiated activity sheets**
This explains the required tasks on the differentiated sheets. It also explains which children will benefit from a specific differentiated sheet.

**Generic sheets**
This provides suggestions for further activities with specific generic sheets to be found at the back of the book.

# Phonicability

## SECTION 1

## Single sounds

# Single sounds

## OVERALL AIMS

- To learn the definition of 'phoneme' and to use the term with ease and confidence.
- To sound, recognise and name single letters.
- To be aware that letter names and letter sounds are not the same.
- To recognise that the upper and lower cases of a letter sound identical.
- To practise and refine the formation of single letters.

## TEACHER'S NOTES

Children enjoy using technical terms and need to familiarise themselves with those that are constantly referred to throughout the National Literacy Framework. It is important that they become confident in using these terms correctly and in an appropriate context. 'Phoneme' is a term that the children need to learn very early in their phonics sessions.

A phoneme is the smallest unit of sound in a word. For example, the word 'man' has three phonemes, 'm', 'a' and 'n'. It is vital that children learn to listen to and sound the phonemes represented by the letters of the alphabet. Ensure that an alphabet chart is displayed in the classroom, preferably with attractive illustrations.

Pronunciation of the single phonemes should be as follows:

- 'b', 'd', 'g', 'j', 'q', 'w' and 'y' should be voiced and quick, ie not 'buh', 'duh' and so on;
- 'a', 'e', 'i', 'l', 'm', 'n', 'o', 'r', 's', 'u', 'v' and 'z' should be voiced and long, ie 'ssss', 'mmmm', 'nnnn' and so on;
- 'c', 'k', 'p', 't' and 'ch' should be voiceless and quick, ie not 'cuh', 'puh' and so on;
- 'f', 'h', 'sh' and 'th' should be voiceless and long, ie 'ffff', 'hhhh', 'shhhh' and 'thhhh';
- 'x' should be pronounced as 'cs'.

## INTENDED LEARNING

- To learn the definition of 'phoneme' and begin to use the term appropriately.
- To listen to, name and sound single letters.
- To recognise that the upper and lower cases of a letter sound the same.
- To name an object that begins with any given sound.

## SUGGESTED ACTIVITIES

- Display letters all over the room in both upper and lower cases. When teaching a letter, ensure that the children do not confuse its name with its sound. It is important to be familiar with the recommended pronunciations in *Phonics, Progression in phonics: materials for whole-class teaching* (DfEE, 1999) before introducing any phoneme. For example, 's' says 'ssss' and not 'suh'; 'p' is spoken voicelessly whereas 'b' is voiced.
- Ask the children to identify items in the classroom which begin with a specific sound. Go on a 'sound hunt' to find objects beginning with the chosen sound. Explain that the correct term for 'sound' is 'phoneme' and that this is the word which will be used from now on.
- Make mobiles of each phoneme with the children, using large-sized letters. Ask the children to draw/write objects beginning with each sound to hang from each letter.
- Make large ladders out of card. Ask the children to add 'rungs' with words/pictures on them with the same beginning phoneme.

- Discuss the meaning of alliteration. Make up alliterative sentences using the children's names.
- Ask the children to cut out pictures of objects from magazines that begin with a particular phoneme. Glue the pictures onto a large piece of paper. Use the pictures to make up alliterative sentences or to make up a story about the things in the picture.
- Play games such as 'I spy' and 'Grandma went to market', naming items that begin with the phoneme being taught.
- Share alphabet books, such as Michael Rosen's *ABC* (Macdonald Young Books, 1995). Hunt for words beginning with the chosen phonemes in the pictures.
- Make a phoneme wall with each row of 'bricks' allocated to a phoneme. Ask each child to write their name on a brick in the appropriate row. Challenge them to add words to the wall over the next few weeks.
- Use stories and rhymes to ask the children to identify words that start with the phoneme being taught.
- Ask the children to make the phoneme being taught from a wide range of materials, such as Plasticine, sandpaper, playdough, sticking dry pasta onto letter-outline, clay and so on.
- Use phonics cards (for example, Early Learning Set, LDA cards, Lotto cards and so on) to play games and reinforce the phoneme being taught.
- Ask the children to bring from home an object beginning with the phoneme being taught. Make a table display. Label the objects. Use these words in spelling, handwriting and discussions throughout the week.

- Use over-writing, tracing or copying sheets to practise the formation of the current phoneme.
- Play 'Phoneme Football': divide the class into two football teams (of the children's choice); ask each child whether a named word begins with the current phoneme. For example, "Manjit, does bird begin with b?" or "Anya, does fish begin with b?" If the child answers correctly, they score a goal. The winning team scores the most goals.
- Make a class shop where the items for sale all begin with the phoneme being taught. Make signs listing the products. Encourage the children to write shopping lists.
- Make a phoneme zoo! Ask the children to find and draw animals that begin with the chosen phoneme. Display this as a mural. Ask the children to write (or the adult can scribe) sentences about each animal. Ask the children to invent an animal of their own!
- Enlarge a page from a newspaper or magazine. Ask the children to cut out all the words beginning with the chosen phoneme. How many did they find? Choose ten of the words and glue them onto card in the shape of a fish. Add five other words that do not begin with this phoneme. The children could then play 'Fishing', keeping the words that begin with the chosen phoneme.

## USING THE DIFFERENTIATED ACTIVITY SHEETS

### Activity sheets a
These are for children who need practice in guided letter formation and repetition of the phoneme being taught.

### Activity sheets b
These are for children whose ability to form letters is more developed. They will be able to do a little more independent writing but still need some guidance.

### Activity sheets c
These are for children who can confidently form letters without any guidance and who will be able to write a few simple words independently.

The mixed activity sheets give further practice and reinforcement of these skills.

## GENERIC SHEETS

- Use Generic sheet 1 to practise letter formation or sentence writing.
- Use Generic sheet 2 to make a cube or a dice. Write one phoneme on each face. The children take turns to roll it and name the phoneme/ write a word/name an object.
- Use Generic sheet 4 to make phoneme cards for Snap or Pelmanism games. Stick the sheet onto card before cutting out the boxes. Write a single phoneme on each pair of cards.
- Use Generic sheet 4 to make phoneme dominoes. Stick the sheet onto card before cutting out the boxes. Draw a line down the centre of each box and write a single phoneme on each half. Ensure that there are at least three identical phonemes to enable the dominoes to match up.
- Use Generic sheet 5 for wordsearches or crosswords. Activity sheets for phonemes 'c' and 's' illustrate these.

◆Draw a big ant.

**Aa**

Write

**A**

**a**

◆ Draw a big ant.

Write

a big ant

Draw an ant with a hat on.
Write this –
*an ant and a hat.*

# A a

Ants in my pants!

Write **A** and **a.**

_____

- - - - - - - - - - - - -

_____

- - - - - - - - - - - - -

◆ Draw Zep and a big ant.

Write

Zep and a big ant.

Zep _____

◆ Write three more **a** words.

_____

_____

Draw an ant with a bag. Write about it.

# Bb

I like big bubbles!

Zep

Write

◆Colour blue all the bubbles with b inside them.

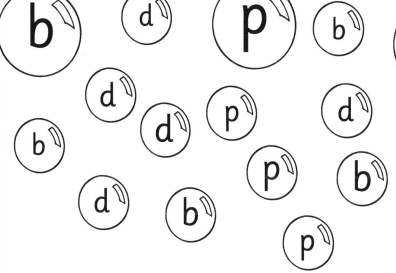

Write

Draw Zep with lots of bubbles.

Write this –
**bubbles.**

# B b

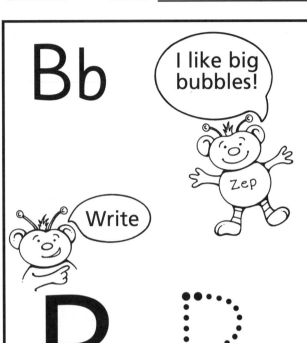

I like big bubbles!

Zep

Write

B

b

◆ Colour blue all the bubbles with B or b in them.

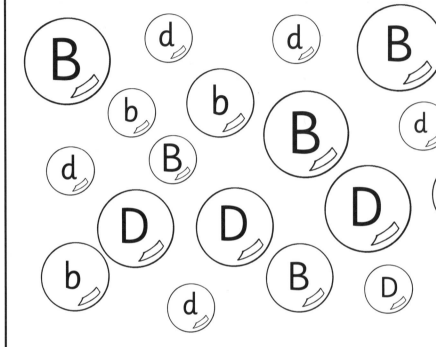

Write

Draw Zep blowing bubbles.

Write a word that starts with b.

Big bubbles

# Bb

◆ Colour blue all the bubbles with a **b** word in them.

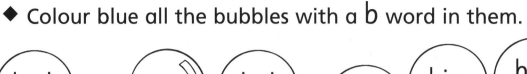

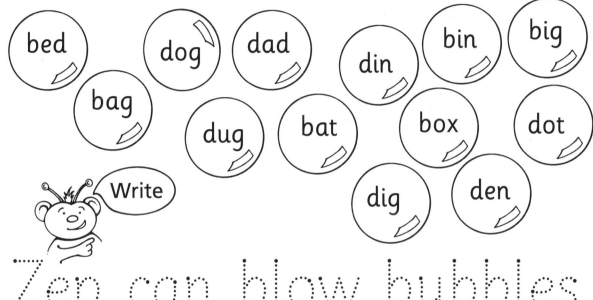

*Zep can blow bubbles.*

# Zep

◆ Write two more **b** words.

_____

_____

# Cc

Cats are clever!

Write

Colour the squares with C in them. There are six.

| c | f | p | c |
|---|---|---|---|
| a | e | c | a |
| m | c | q | d |
| c | u | o | c |

Draw a cat.

Write

Draw Zep with a cat.

Write this – cat.

# Cc

Cats are clever!

Write

C c C c

C c

Find the **C** words and colour them in.
One has been done for you.

| c | a | t | p |
|---|---|---|---|
| d | c | u | p |
| c | u | t | f |
| c | o | t | g |

cut
cat
cup
cot

Write

cat

cup

cot

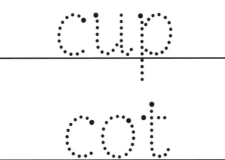

Draw Zep in a cot.
Write a word that starts with C.

# Cc

Cats are clever!

Write **C** and **c.**

_____

_____

_____

_____

◆ Find the C words and colour them in. One has been done for you.

| d | e | c | a | t |
|---|---|---|---|---|
| c | u | p | g | h |
| f | c | c | a | p |
| m | c | u | t | c |
| c | c | o | t | c |
| o | c | c | a | n |

cut
cup
cot
cat
cap
can

Write

Zep can wear a cap.

Zep _____

◆ Write two more C words.

_____

_____

Draw a cat in a cot.

16

◆ Draw a big dog.

# Dd

What a droopy dog!

Write

## Dd Dd

## Dd

◆Draw a big dog.

Write

Draw a dog that can dig.
Write a word that starts with d.

a big dog

# Dd

What a droopy dog!

Write Dd.

_____

- - - - - - - - - - - - - -

_____

_____

◆ Draw Zep and a big dog.

Write

Zep and a big dog.

## Zep

◆ Write two more d words.

_____

_____

Draw a dog and a dad who can dig.

# E e

Eggs are excellent!

Write

◆ Colour yellow all the eggs with e inside them.

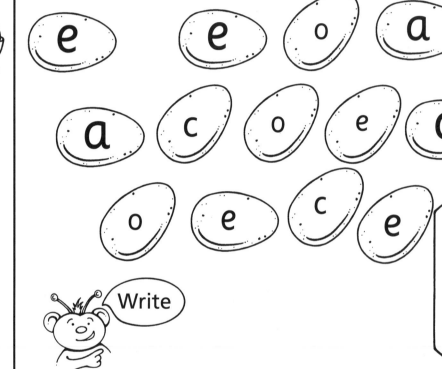

Write

Draw Zep with six eggs.
Write this –
eggs.

# E e

Eggs are excellent!

Write

Ee Ee

Ee

◆Colour yellow all the eggs with E or e in them.

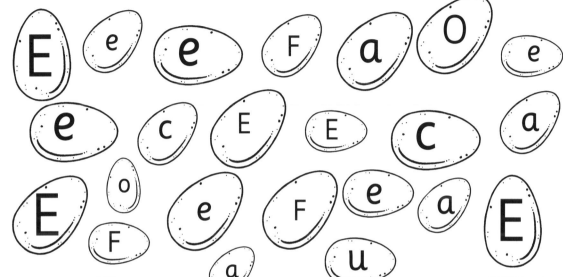

Write

Zep's eggs

Draw Zep and an egg. Write a word that starts with e.

# Ee

Write Ee.

◆ Colour yellow all the eggs with **e** words in them.

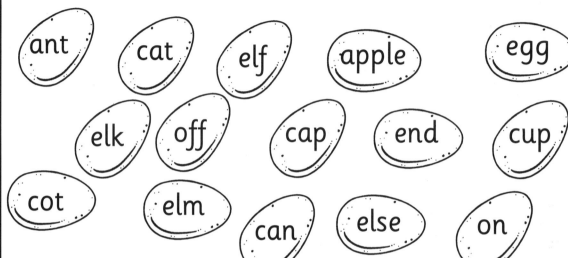

ant    cat    elf    apple    egg

elk    off    cap    end    cup

cot    elm    can    else    on

Write

Eggs are excellent.

Eggs _____

Draw six eggs in a box. Write some words beginning with **e**.

22

# F f

I wish I had fish in my dish!

Write

◆ Write f to finish the words.

_ish        _og        _un

◆ Colour green the fish scales with f in them.

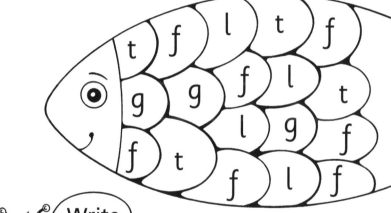

Write

fish

Draw a big fish.

Write this – fish.

Name _____    Date _____

24

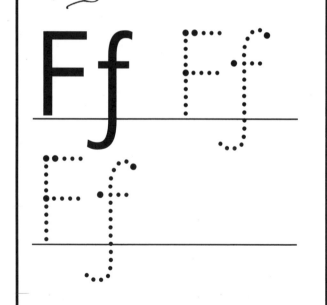

◆ Write ƒ to finish the words.

__an     __in     __ish     __og     __rog

◆ Colour green the fish scales with F or ƒ in them.

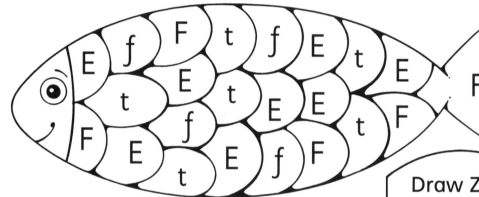

 Write

Fish can swim.

Draw Zep with a big fish.

Write a word that starts with ƒ.

# Ff

I wish I had fish in my dish!

Write Ff.

◆ Write ƒ to finish the words.

_ish          _an          _ed          _in
_rog          _unny          _luffy          _all

Colour green the fish scales with ƒ words in them.

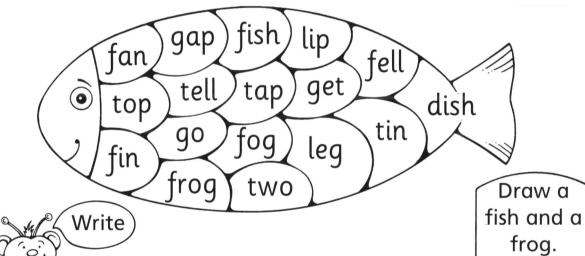

fan  gap  fish  lip  fell
top  tell  tap  get  dish
fin  go  fog  leg  tin
frog  two

Write

Fish swim in water.

Fish

Draw a fish and a frog. Write more ƒ words.

# Gg

Grass is green.

Zep

Write

◆ Find the squares with g in them and colour them in. There are six.

| f | g | h | g |
|---|---|---|---|
| q | b | g | y |
| d | g | t | q |
| g | p | g | h |

Draw a green hat.

Zep

Write

green

Draw Zep in a green hat. Write this – green.

Gg

Grass is green.

1 zep

Write

# Gg Gg

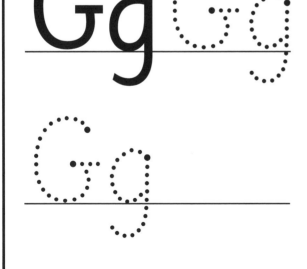

Gg

◆ Find the **g** words and colour them in.
One has been done for you.

| d | g | u | m |
|---|---|---|---|
| f | g | a | s |
| g | o | t | d |
| t | g | e | t |

gas

got

gum

get

Write

get

gum.

got

Draw Zep in a green hat.
Write a word that starts with **g**.

# Gg

Grass is green.

Write Gg.

1 zep

♦ Find the **g** words and colour them in.
One has been done for you.

| g | r | a | s | s |
|---|---|---|---|---|
| d | g | r | i | n |
| f | g | u | m | g |
| g | o | t | g | m |
| g | r | e | e | n |
| t | g | g | e | t |

~~green~~
gum
got
grass
get
grin

 Write

Grass is green.

## Grass

Draw a green tree and some green grass.
Write words beginning with **g**.

# Hh

Do horses live in houses?

Zep

Write

◆ Write h to finish the words.

_at          _ouse          _and          _orse

◆ Draw a house on a hill.

Write

house

Draw Zep and a hedgehog. Write this – **house**.

# Hh

Do horses live in houses?

Zep

Write

Hh Hh

Hh

◆ Write h to finish the words.

_ouse          _and          _orse          _olly

_en          _ook

◆ Draw a house on a hill.

Draw a horse and some hay. Write a word that starts with h.

Write

a house on a hill

H h

Do horses live in houses?

Zep

Write Hh.

◆ Write h to finish the words.

_at

_ouse

_ose

_ook

_en

_eel

_air

_and

Write

Do horses live in houses?

◆ Draw Zep and a hedgehog.

Draw a horse eating hay. Write more h words.

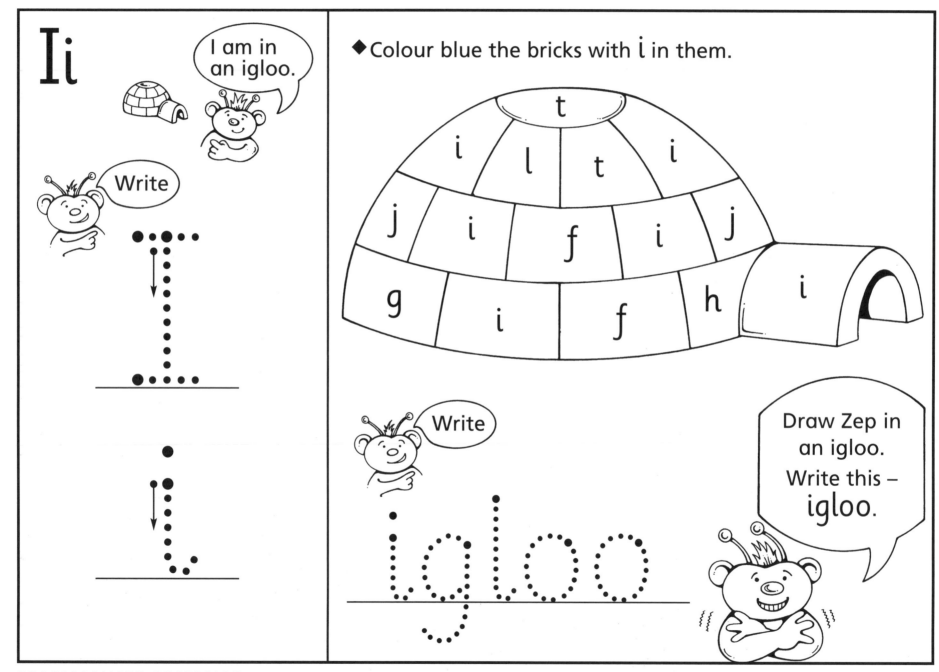

# Ii

I am in an igloo.

Write

Colour blue the bricks with i in them.

Write

Draw Zep in an igloo.
Write this –
igloo.

**Ii**

I am in an igloo.

Write

**Ii**

◆ Colour blue the bricks with **I** or **i** in them.

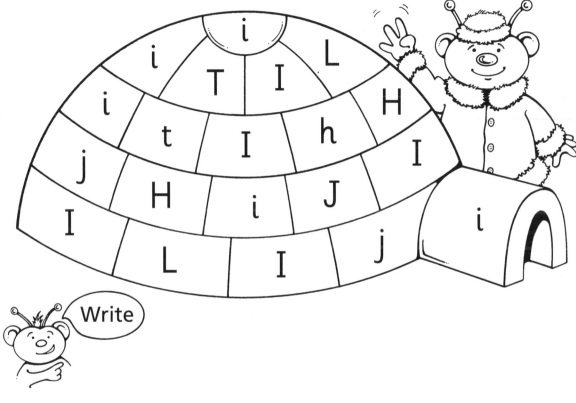

Write

Zep is in an igloo.

◆ Draw Zep in an igloo.
◆ Write more **i** words.

# Ii

*I am in an igloo.*

*Write Ii.*

◆ Colour blue the bricks with **i** words in them.

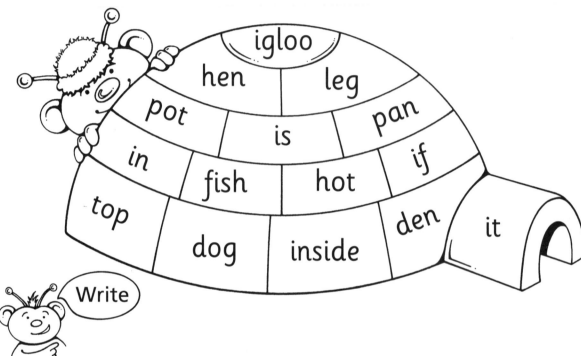

igloo

hen | leg
pot | is | pan
in | fish | hot | if
top | dog | inside | den | it

*Write*

Zep is in an igloo.

Zep

◆ Write two more **i** words.

◆ Draw Zep in an igloo.

_____  _____

# Jj

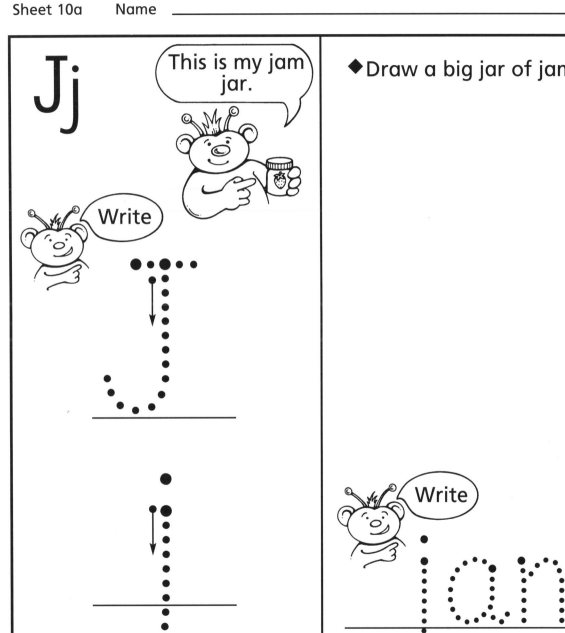

This is my jam jar.

Write

◆Draw a big jar of jam.

Write

jam

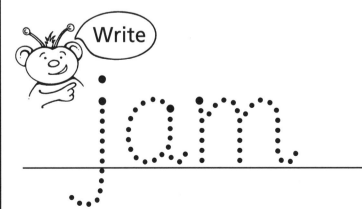

Draw a jelly that jiggles.
Write this –
jelly.

**J j**

This is my jam jar.

Write

J j

◆ Draw a big jar of jam.

Write

a big jar of jam.

Draw a jelly that jiggles. Write another j word.

J j

Write J j.

This is my jam jar.

◆ Draw a big jar of jam.

Write

Zep and a big jar of jam.

Zep _____

◆ Write two more j words.

_____

_____

Draw Zep with a jelly that jiggles.

# Kk

Write

◆ Write k to finish the words.

_ite          _ing          _ey

◆ Colour red all the kites with k in them.

Write

kite

◆ Draw a big red kite.
◆ Write this –
king.

38

K k

Write

Kk Kk

_____

_____

_____

◆ Write k to finish the words.

_ite          _ey          _itten

◆ Colour red all the kites with K or k in them.

Write

Kites fly.

◆ Draw a big red kite.
◆ Write another k word.

Write Kk.

Do kings fly kites?

_____

- - - - - - - - - - - - - -

_____

- - - - - - - - - - - - - -

_____

◆ Write **k** to finish the words.

 _ey     _itten     _ennel     _ite

 _angaroo

◆ Colour red all the kites with a **k** word in them.

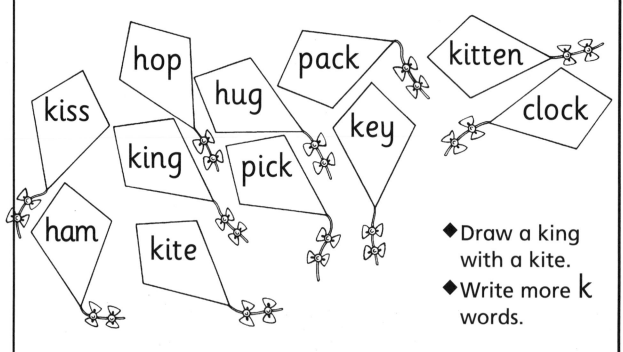

◆ Draw a king with a kite.

◆ Write more **k** words.

**L l**

Look at my little lamb.

1 Zep

Write

Find the squares with **l** in them and colour them in. There are six.

| h | l | f | b | l |
|---|---|---|---|---|
| b | t | l | h | k |
| l | d | k | d | t |
| d | f | l | t | h |
| h | k | b | l | f |

◆ Draw a lamb.

Write

lamb

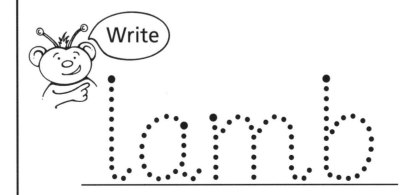

Draw Zep and a lamb.

Write this –

lamb.

# L l

Look at my little lamb.

Write

L l l̇.....l̇

_____

_____

◆ Find the **l** words and colour them in. One has been done for you.

| l | o | r | r | y |
|---|---|---|---|---|
| o | l | l | e | g |
| m | l | o | o | k |
| h | l | a | m | b |
| t | l | o | g | e |

~~lamb~~
leg
look
log
lorry

Write

l̇a̤m̈b̈

l̇o̤o̤k̈

l̇o̤r̈r̈ÿ

Draw Zep and a lamb. Write another **l** word.

42

# Ll

Look at my little lamb.

Write L and l.

◆ Find the l words and colour them in. One has been done for you.

| h | l | e | m | o | n |
|---|---|---|---|---|---|
| o | l | l | e | g | p |
| l | a | m | b | f | l |
| l | o | l | o | g | l |
| p | l | l | o | o | k |
| l | a | d | d | e | r |

~~lamb~~

ladder

leg

lemon

look

log

◆ Write four more l words.

_____

_____

_____

_____

Draw a lady on a ladder.

# Mm

This is me on a mat with a mop.

Write

◆ Write **m** to do the crosswords.

|   | o | p |
|---|---|---|
|   |   |   |
|   | a | n |

|   | a | t |
|---|---|---|
|   |   |   |
|   | a | p |

◆ Draw a man.

Write

**man**

Draw a man with a map.
Write this –
**man.**

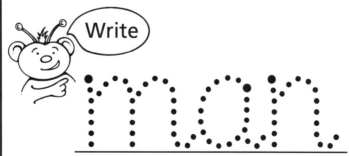

PHONICABILITY RECEPTION

Mm

This is me on the moon with a mouse.

Write

# Mm

Mm

◆ Write **m** to do the crossword.

| | | o | u | s | e |
| e | | | | | |
| n | | | | | |
| | | | | | |
| | o | o | n | | |

◆ Draw a mouse in a mug.

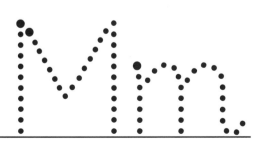

Draw a man on the moon. Write another **m** word.

# Mm

I've got some milk in my mug.

Write Mm.

_____

- - - - - - - - - - - -

_____

- - - - - - - - - - - -

◆ Write m to do the crossword.

| | i | l | k | |
|---|---|---|---|---|
| u | | | | |
| | a | t | | o |
| | | | | p |
| | u | g | | |

Draw a mosquito.

◆ Write the words.

_____

_____

_____

_____

_____

Draw a man with a map.
Write more m words.

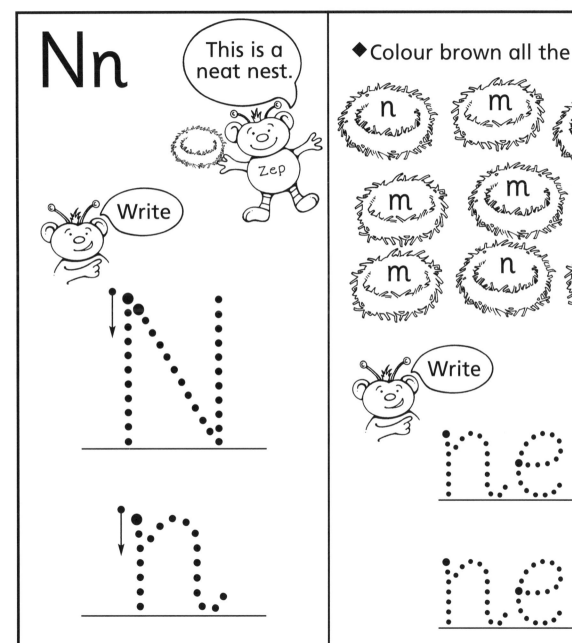

# Nn

This is a neat nest.

Write

Colour brown all the nests with n inside them.

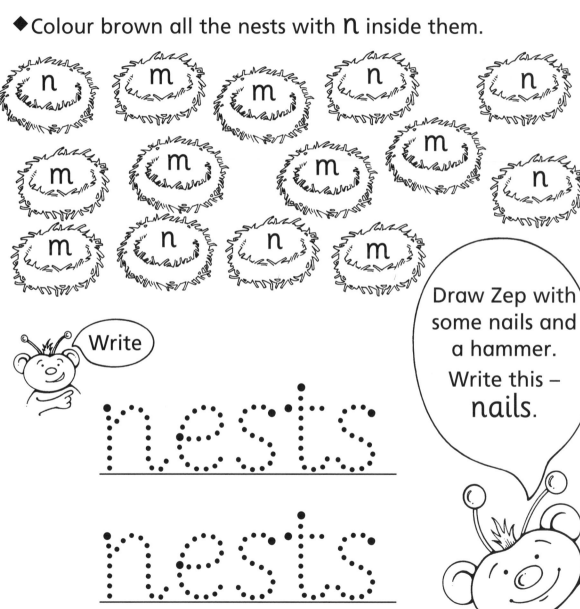

Write

nests

nests

Draw Zep with some nails and a hammer. Write this – nails.

PHONICABILITY RECEPTION

Nn

This is a neat nest.

Zep

Write

N n

_____

_____

◆ Colour brown all the nests with N or n in them.

m  M  N  n  M

m  m  N  M  N

m  n  M  n

N  M  M  m

M  m  n  N  M

n  M

Write

This is a nice nest.

◆ Write a new n word.

_____

◆ Draw Zep with nails and a hammer.
◆ Write another n word.

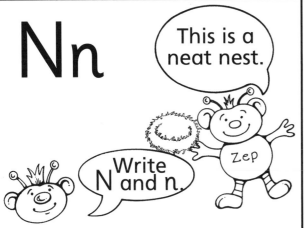

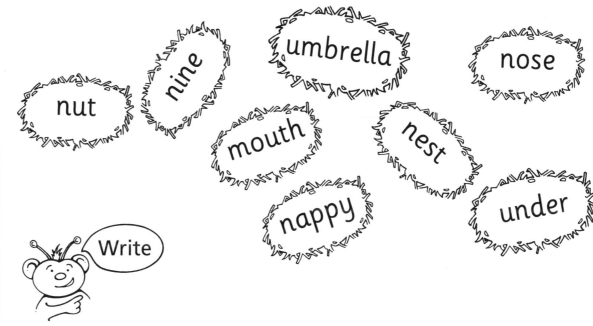

◆Colour brown all the nests with **n** words in them.

Write

Nine nuts in a nest.

◆Draw nine nuts in a nest.
◆Write more **n** words.

# Oo

This is an orange octopus.

Write

◆ Draw an octopus. Make it orange.

Write

octopus

O

Draw Zep and an octopus. Write this – octopus.

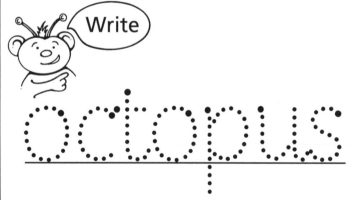

# Oo

This is an orange octopus.

Write

Oo Oo Oo

_____

Oo

_____

_____

◆ Draw an octopus. Make it orange.

Write

an octopus

_____

an _____

Draw Zep and an octopus. Write another **O** word.

# Oo

Write O and o.

This is an orange octopus.

_____

- - - - - - - - - - - - -

_____

- - - - - - - - - - - - -

◆ Draw Zep and an octopus. Make the octopus orange.

Write the sentence.

Is an octopus orange?

Is _____

◆ Write two more O words.

_____

_____

Draw an octopus with an orange.

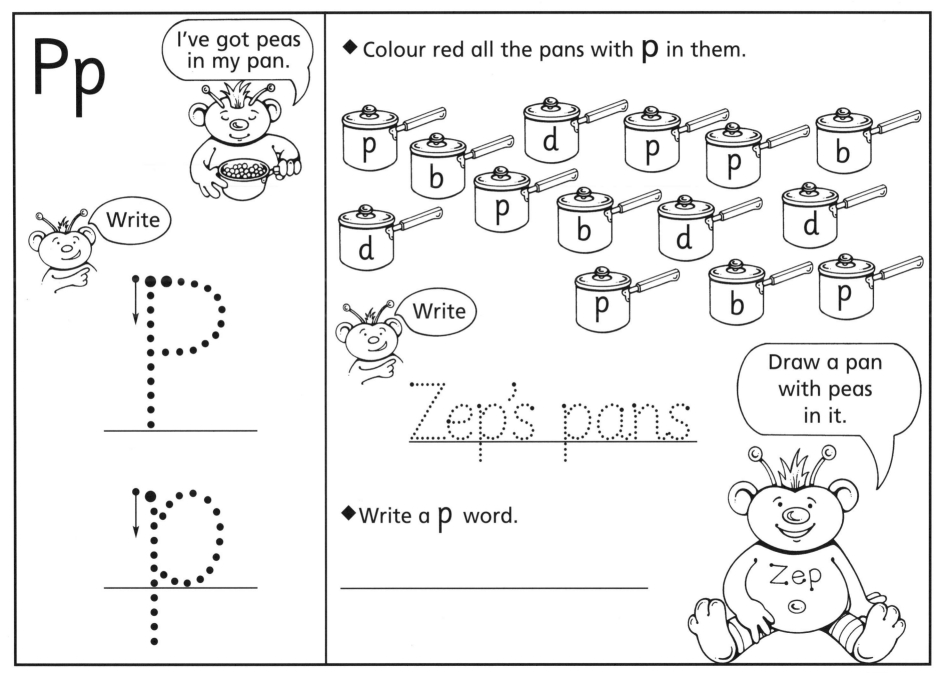

# Pp

I've got peas in my pan.

Write

◆ Colour red all the pans with **p** in them.

Write

Zep's pans

◆ Write a **p** word.

_____

Draw a pan with peas in it.

Zep

54

# P p

I've got peas in my pan.

Write

# P p P p

_____

_____

◆ Colour red all the pans with P or p in them.

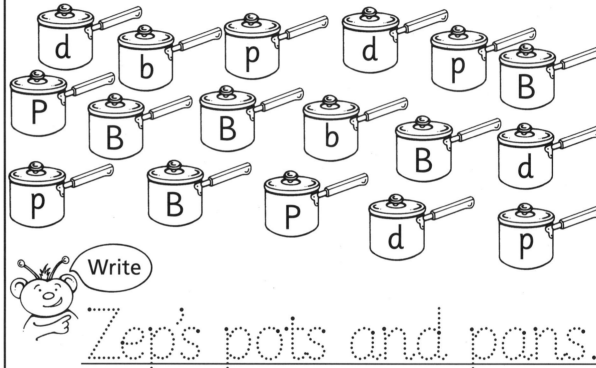

Write

Zep's pots and pans.

◆ Draw Zep's pots and pans.

Draw a pan with peas in it. Write more p words.

# Pp

I've got peas in my pan.

Write Pp.

◆ Colour red all the pans with a **p** word in them.

dog   puppy   bed   peg

pin   bin   play   den

Write these **p** words.

pot   pin

pan   peg

◆ Write two more.

_____

_____

Draw Zep with a pan of peas.

This queen is green!

Zep

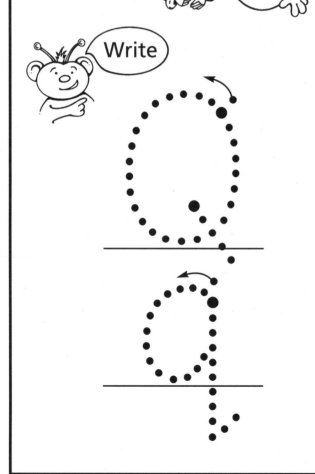

Write

Write

◆ Find the squares with q in them and colour them in. There are seven.

| b | q | d | b | p |
|---|---|---|---|---|
| d | b | p | d | q |
| q | d | q | b | p |
| q | p | d | b | q |
| p | b | d | q | b |

◆ Draw a queen.

Draw Zep under a quilt. Write this – queen.

# Qq

This queen is green!

Zep

Write

# Qq

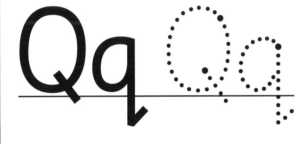

_____

_____

◆ Find the **q** words and colour them in. One has been done for you.

| g | q | u | i | t | p |
|---|---|---|---|---|---|
| p | q | u | i | l | t |
| b | q | u | i | z | d |
| q | u | e | e | n | b |
| d | q | u | i | c | k |

~~quit~~

quiz

queen

quick

quilt

Write

queen

quilt

Draw a queen under a quilt. Write another **q** word.

# Qq

This queen is green!

Write Qq.

_____

- - - - - - - - - - - - - - - -

_____

- - - - - - - - - - - - - - - -

_____

◆ Find the **q** words and colour them in. One has been done for you.

| p | q | u | i | e | t |
|---|---|---|---|---|---|
| q | u | i | t | p | b |
| p | q | u | i | c | k |
| q | u | i | l | t | b |
| b | q | u | i | z | d |
| q | u | e | e | n | b |

quiet
queen
quick
quiz
quilt
quit

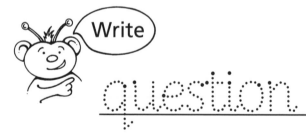

Write

question

queen

quilt

Draw a queen under a quilt. Write more **q** words.

◆ Write **r** to finish the words.

_ed      _at      _un

◆ Colour red where the roof has **r**.

Draw Zep and a robot.
Write this –
**red robot.**

# R r

Here's a red robot.

Write

R r   R r

R r

◆ Write **r** to finish the words.

\_at     \_ug     \_ocket     \_abbit

◆ Colour red where the roof has **R** or **r**.

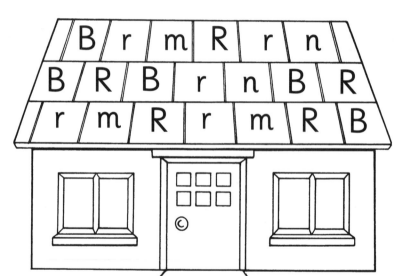

| B | r | m | R | r | n |
| B | R | B | r | n | B | R |
| r | m | R | r | m | R | B |

Write

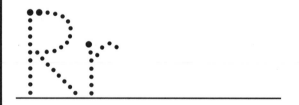

robot

r

Draw Zep and a robot. Write another **r** word.

60

# Rr

Write Rr.

Here's a red robot.

_____

_____

_____

_____

_____

◆ Write r to finish the words.

 __abbit

 __ocket

 __ailway

 __ing

 __obot

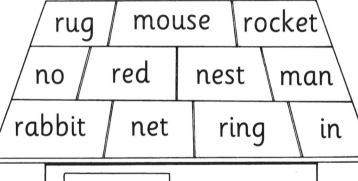 __un

| rug | mouse | rocket |
|-----|-------|--------|
| no | red | nest | man |
| rabbit | net | ring | in |

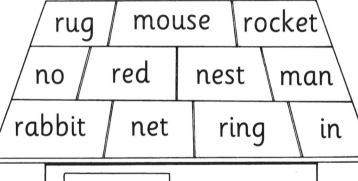

◆ Colour red where the roof has a r word.

Draw Zep and a red robot. Write more r words.

61

**Ss**

I saw the sun and some stars!

Zep

Write

◆ Write S to do the crosswords.

Draw a star.

Write

Draw a star and the sun. Write this – star and sun.

Zep

**Ss**

I saw the sun and some stars!

Write

**Ss**  **Ss**

Ss

◆ Write S to do the crossword.

|   | t | o | p |   |
|---|---|---|---|---|
| t |   |   |   |   |
| a |   |   | u | n |
| r |   |   |   |   |
|   |   | k | i | p |

Draw a sad man.

Draw a sad sausage. Write another S word.

**Ss**

*Write Ss.*

*I saw the sun and some stars!*

Zep

◆ Write **S** to do the crossword.

| | t | o | p | |
|---|---|---|---|---|
| t | | | | |
| a | | | | e |
| r | | u | | a |
| | a | n | d | |

◆ Draw a sad sausage.

◆ Write the words.

S _____

S _____

_____

_____

_____

◆ Draw a sausage with a scarf.

◆ Write more **S** words.

64

# Tt

I've got tiny teeth.

Zep

Write

◆ Draw a teddy with two teeth.

Draw a red tent.
Write this –
tent.

Write

two teeth

# T t

I've got tiny teeth.

Write

Zep

T t    T t

T t

◆ Draw a teddy with two teeth.

Write

a tap

and two teeth

Draw two tins with red tops. Write another t word.

Write Tt.

I've got tiny teeth.

Zep

◆ Draw two taps and ten tiny teddies.

Write what you drew.

two _____

_____

◆Draw two tins with red tops.
◆Write more t words.

# Uu

I'm under an umbrella.

Write

◆ Colour the umbrellas with U in them.

Write

umbrellas

Draw an upside-down umbrella.
Write this – umbrella.

# U u

**Write**

U u

U u

_____

_____

◆ Colour the umbrellas with U or u in them.

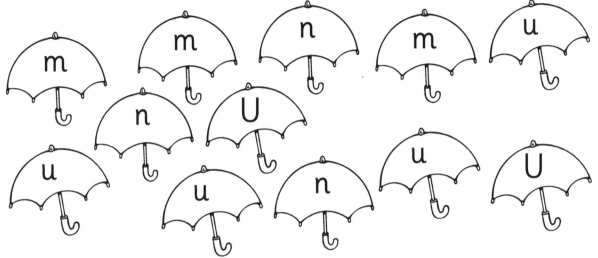

◆ How many umbrellas have u in them?

____ umbrellas have u in them.

**Write**

six umbrellas

◆ Draw an upside-down umbrella.

◆ Write another u word.

# Uu

Write
Uu.

I'm under an
umbrella.

_____

- - - - - - - - - - - - - - - -

_____

- - - - - - - - - - - - - - - -

_____

◆Colour the umbrellas with U words in them.

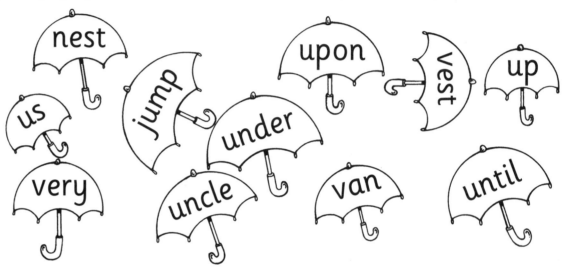

nest   jump   upon   vest   up
us   under   uncle   van   until
very

◆Write some of the words you coloured.

_____ _____ _____

_____ _____ _____

◆Write two more.

_____ _____

◆Draw an
untidy
umbrella.

# Vv

This vest is my very best!

Write

◆ Find the squares with V in them. There are seven. Colour them in.

| v | m | c | n | v |
|---|---|---|---|---|
| c | u | v | n | u |
| a | v | c | v | u |
| n | a | m | u | v |
| u | v | a | u | n |

◆ Draw a red van.

Write

a red van.

Draw Zep in a green van.
Write this –
van.

72

# V v

This vest is my very best!

Write

# V v  Vv

_____

_____

_____

◆ Find the V words and colour them in. One has been done for you.

| v | o | i | c | e | u |
|---|---|---|---|---|---|
| a | v | v | a | n | v |
| u | v | a | s | e | s |
| s | v | i | l | u | e |
| m | u | v | e | s | t |
| n | v | e | r | y | v |

~~voice~~

vest

vase

van

very

Write

vest

_____

vase

_____

Draw Zep in a green vest. Write another V word.

# V v

This vest is my very best!

Write Vv.

------------------------

------------------------

------------------------

------------------------

◆ Find the V words and colour them in. One has been done for you.

| v | a | s | e | v | m |
|---|---|---|---|---|---|
| v | v | e | s | t | t |
| v | v | i | l | u | e |
| v | v | o | i | c | e |
| u | v | v | e | r | y |
| e | m | v | v | a | n |

~~voice~~

very

vase

van

vest

 Write

very

vest

van

Draw Zep in a vest in a van. Write more V words.

# Ww

I want to walk on the wall.

Write

◆ Write W to finish the words.

___eb     ___all     ___ell     ___atch

◆ Colour blue where the web has W.

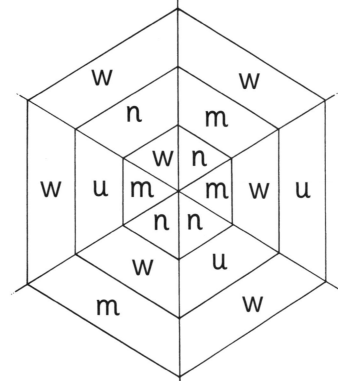

Draw Zep and a web.
Write this –
**web.**

Write

PHONICABILITY RECEPTION

# Ww

I want to walk on the wall.

Write

# Ww

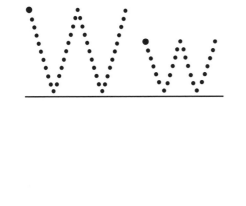

◆ Write W to finish the words.

_eb     _all     _ell     _atch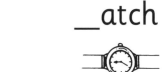

◆ Colour blue where the web has W.

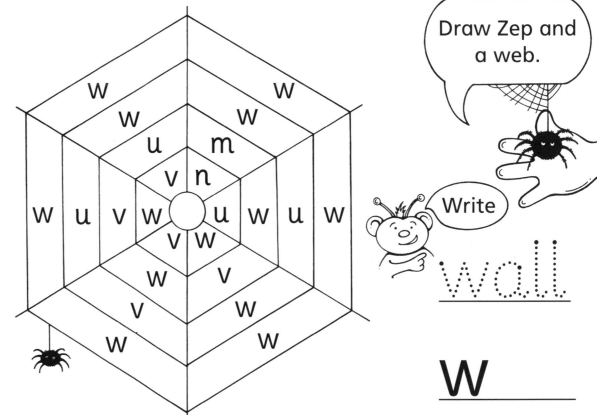

Draw Zep and a web.

Write

wall

W ___

Sheet 23c    Name _____     Date _____

# Ww

Write Ww.

I want to walk on the wall.

◆ Write W to finish the words.

 __eb     __all     __heel

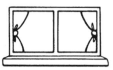 __indow     __ell     __atch

◆ Draw a wolf.

Draw a wolf in the wood. Write more W words.

PHONICABILITY RECEPTION

# Xx

There's a fox in this box!

Write

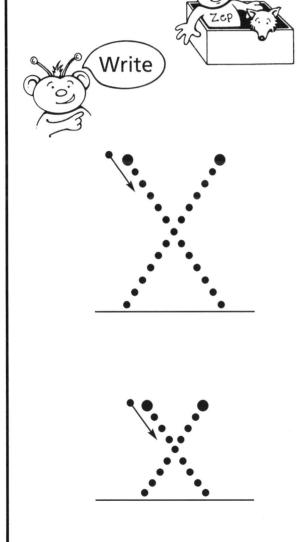

◆ Write X to do the crosswords.

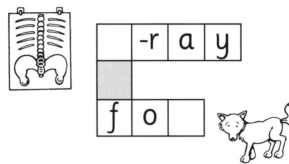

| | -r | a | y |
| | | | |
| f | o | | |

| b | o | |
| | | |
| s | i | |

6

◆ Draw Zep's x-ray.

Write

x-ray

Draw a fox in a box.
Write this –
fox.

PHONICABILITY RECEPTION

78

Xx

There's a fox in this box!

Write

Xx ⋮⋮

_____

_____

◆ Write X to do the crossword.

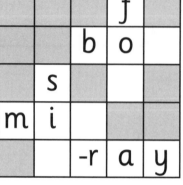

|   |   |   | f |   |
|---|---|---|---|---|
|   |   | b | o |   |
|   | s |   |   |   |
| m | i |   |   |   |
|   |   | -r | a | y |

6

◆ Draw six boxes.

Draw a fox in a box.
Write another X word.

# Xx

Write Xx.

There's a fox in this box!

Zep

◆ Write X to do the crossword.

| | f | | | | |
|---|---|---|---|---|---|
| m | i | | | f | |
| | | | b | o | |
| s | | | | | |
| i | | | | | |
| | -r | a | y | | |

◆ Draw six boxes.

◆ Write the words.

_____

_____

_____

_____

_____

Draw Zep and a fox in a box.

Write more X words.

80

# Y y

I love yellow yoghurt.

Write

◆ Colour yellow the yoghurts with **y** in them.

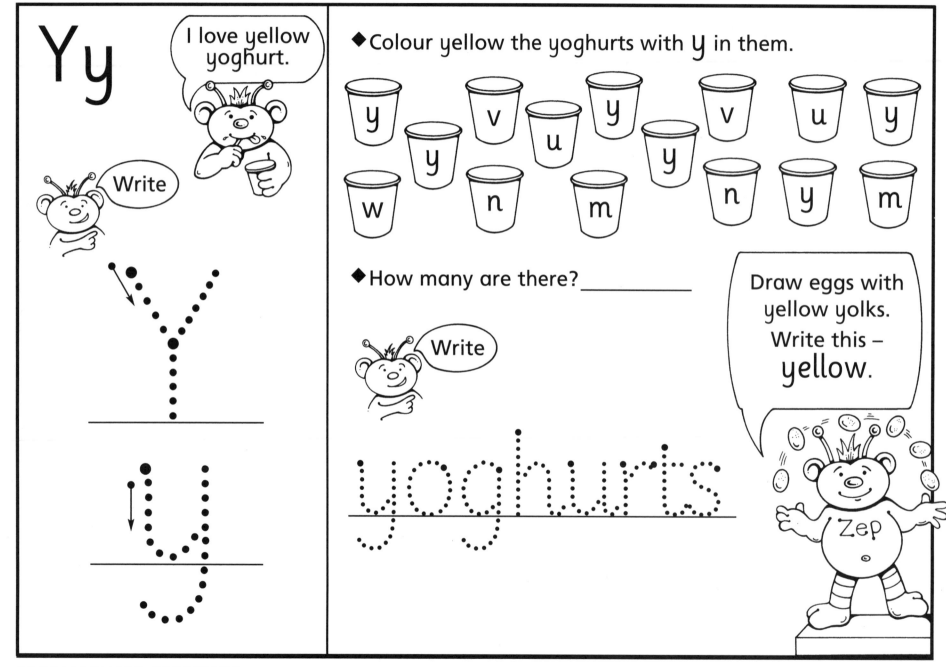

◆ How many are there? _____

Write

Draw eggs with yellow yolks. Write this – **yellow**.

yoghurts

Zep

Y y

I love yellow yoghurt.

Write

# Y y

_____

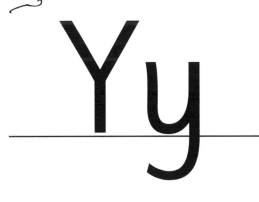

_____

◆ Colour yellow the yoghurts with **y** in them.

y    y    v    w    y    u    y    w

w    w    u    v    y    u    m    y    y

◆ How many are there? _____

Write

yummy

yoghurts

Draw eight eggs with yellow yolks. Write another **y** word.

# Y y

Write Yy.

I love yellow yoghurt.

◆ Colour yellow the yoghurts with Y words in them.

up    yummy    no    out    yes    van

yoghurt    vest    yo-yo    you    under

◆ Write these Y words.

_yellow_    _yoghurt_

_yours_    _yummy_

◆ Write two more.

_____    _____

Draw a yellow yo-yo and a yummy yoghurt.

# Zz

My name is Zep.

Write

◆ Colour the squares with Z in them. There are seven.

| s | u | z | c | m | z |
|---|---|---|---|---|---|
| z | v | w | s | u | s |
| s | w | m | z | u | c |
| s | m | n | a | w | v |
| u | z | m | w | s | z |
| z | m | u | w | v | n |

Draw a red zigzag.

Draw Zep in a zoo.
Write this –
zigzag.

Zz

My name is Zep.

Write

Z z

_____

_____

◆ Find the Z words and colour them in.

| m | z | i | p | u | v |
|---|---|---|---|---|---|
| o | s | z | e | r | o |
| z | i | g | z | a | g |
| o | m | z | Z | e | p |
| z | o | o | p | u | w |
| s | z | e | b | r | a |

zip
Zep
zebra
zoo
zero
zigzag

Write

zero

zebra

Draw Zep in a zoo.
Write another Z word.

# Zz

Write Zz.

My name is Zep.

Zep

◆ Find the Z words and colour them in.

| Z | e | p | u | z | o | o |
|---|---|---|---|---|---|---|
| s | z | i | g | z | a | g |
| u | m | z | e | r | o | z |
| s | z | e | b | r | a | z |
| z | o | o | m | u | p | n |
| s | z | i | p | z | i | g |

zigzag
Zep
zebra
zoo
zero
zoom
zip

Write

zebra

zoo

zero

Draw Zep and a zebra in a zoo.
Write more **Z** words.

PHONICABILITY RECEPTION

◆Draw a line from each picture to its beginning sound.

  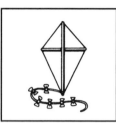  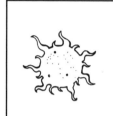 

# abcdefghijklmnopqrstuvwxyz

     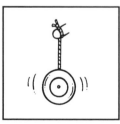

◆Write the words.

__at      __an      __un      __ish

◆Write the beginning sound for each picture.

a
b
c
d
e
f
g
h
i
j
k
l
m

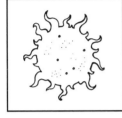      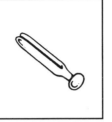    

_un    _at    _an    _eg    _in    _ueen

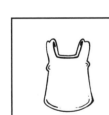      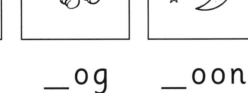  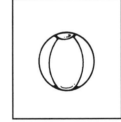  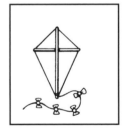

_est    _ouse    _og    _oon    _all    _ite

n
o
p
q
r
s
t
u
v
w
x
y
z

◆Draw things that begin
with e, n and t.

Sheet 27c     Name _____          Date _____

◆Write the beginning sound for each picture.

a b c d e f g h i j k l m

   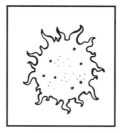 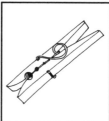 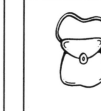

_____ _____ _____ _____ _____ _____

_____ _____ _____ _____ _____ _____

◆Make up some words.    c____  m____  p____  t____

n o p q r s t u v w x y z

PHONICABILITY RECEPTION

# Phonicability

## SECTION 2

# Consonant digraphs
## – ch, sh and th

# Consonant digraphs
## 'ch', 'sh', 'th'

## OVERALL AIMS

❍ To sound, recognise and name the consonant digraphs 'ch', 'sh' and 'th'.
❍ To name and write words that begin with 'ch', 'sh' or 'th'.
❍ To be familiar with the term 'digraph' and to use it appropriately and with confidence.

## TEACHER'S NOTES

Children enjoy using technical terms and need to familiarise themselves with those that are constantly referred to throughout the *National Literacy Framework*. It is important that they become confident in using these terms correctly and in an appropriate context.

'Digraph' is a term that the children need to learn very early in their phonics sessions. It is vital that they learn to listen to and sound the phonemes represented by digraphs. A digraph consists of two letters giving only one phoneme (sound). For example, 'sh' is a consonant digraph, while 'oa' (as in 'coat') is a vowel digraph.

When the session reaches the point of using the activity sheets, read the instructions on each sheet to the groups. Children of Reception age have expressive and receptive language skills far in advance of their reading and writing ability. While not necessarily being able to read the instructions at this stage, the children will easily understand the instructions on the sheets if read out to them.

## INTENDED LEARNING

❍ To listen to, name and sound the digraphs 'ch', 'sh' and 'th'.
❍ To know what the term 'digraph' means and begin to use it appropriately.
❍ To name a word or object that begins with 'ch', 'sh' and 'th'.
❍ To practise writing the letters representing the digraph.
❍ To practise using the digraph as the initial phoneme of a word.

## SUGGESTED ACTIVITIES

❍ Write the digraph being taught on the board and tell the children what phoneme it makes. Explain that the correct term for the two letters making a single phoneme is 'digraph' and that this is the word which will be used from now on. Ask several children to write the letters on the board, saying the digraph out loud. Then ask the rest of the children "What phoneme does this digraph make?" Ask them to think of words that begin with that phoneme. List them on the board. Challenge the children to add words to the list over the next few days.
❍ Enlarge a page of a magazine or newspaper. Ask the children to work in pairs to find and cut out all the words beginning with a chosen digraph. Select appropriate words from the collection and ask the children to draw a picture for each word. Glue the words and pictures into a book to make a class picture dictionary (for example, *Our dictionary of 'th' words*).

❍ Ask the children to use dictionaries to find words that begin with the digraph being taught. Make up a shared class list. Use the words in spelling, handwriting and sentence activities throughout the week. Challenge the children to make alliterative sentences using the words, for example 'Sharon sheep shook the shampoo.'
❍ Make a long 'railway track' around the walls. Put a picture of a train at one end. Either the children or the adult should write words that begin with the current digraph in sections of the track. Encourage the children to use these words in their writing.
❍ Ask the children to cut out pictures of things that begin with the chosen digraph. Challenge them to make up stories/sentences using the pictures, either orally or written. How many of the pictures can they use in one story/sentence?
❍ Ask the children to use dictionaries to find words where the digraph comes at the end of the word. Make a class list of these. Make two ladders to display on the wall – one with words written on the rungs that begin with the digraph and one where the words end with the digraph. Ask the children to make up sentences orally, using one word from each ladder. How many different sentences can they make?
❍ Ask the children to make the digraph being taught from a wide range of materials, such as Plasticine, sandpaper, playdough, clay, by sticking dry pasta onto letter-outline and so on.
❍ Ask the children to find objects in the room/school that begin with the digraph being taught. Put them on display. The children could make labels for each object. Ask them to match the labels to the objects.

❍ Give each child an outline of something beginning with the current digraph, for example a sheep, a bunch of cherries, a thistle. Ask them to write the digraph in the centre of the picture.

❍ Ask the children to look through their current reading book or a chosen library book, for the words beginning or ending with the current digraph. Ask them to write down the words. Ask them to learn some/all of the words by using the 'look, say, cover, write, check' method.

❍ Make some cards with word endings on them, for example '–ing', '–op', '–ip', '–in', '–ut' and '–ick'. Write the chosen digraph, such as 'sh' on another card. Ask the children to match the beginnings to the endings to see how many words they can make (shop, ship, shin, shut).

❍ Make a class story book using as many words as possible with the chosen digraph. Ask the children to illustrate it. Share the book to reinforce words.

❍ Share poems that contain the chosen digraph, such as 'Teeth' by Wendy Cope (First Verses compiled by John Foster, Oxford University Press, 1996). Ask the children to act out and overemphasise the 'Chomp, chomp, chomp' part of each verse. They could make up further verses or change the existing verses.

## USING THE DIFFERENTIATED ACTIVITY SHEETS

### Activity sheets a

These are for children who need practice in guided letter formation and repetition of the digraph being taught. They also encourage them to build up words from the digraph and other given letters.

### Activity sheets b

These are for children whose ability to form letters is more developed. They will be able to do a little more independent writing but still need some guidance. The sheets encourage them to build up words from the digraph and other given letters and also to find new words from the digraph.

### Activity sheets c

These are for children who can confidently form letters without any guidance and who will be able to write a few words independently. They encourage them to build up words from the digraph and other given letters and also to find new words from the digraph.

The mixed activity sheets give further practice and reinforcement of these skills.

### GENERIC SHEETS

❍ Use Generic sheet 1 to practise letter formation or sentence writing.

❍ Use Generic sheet 4 to make digraph cards for Snap or Pelmanism games. Stick the sheet onto card before cutting out the boxes. Write a digraph on each pair of cards. Mix in some single phoneme cards for extra difficulty.

❍ Use Generic sheet 4 to make digraph dominoes. Stick the sheet onto card before cutting out the boxes. Draw a line down the centre of each box and write a digraph on each half. Mix some single phonemes in to add difficulty.

❍ Use Generic sheet 5 for wordsearches or crosswords. Activity sheets for phonemes 'c' and 's' illustrate these.

❍ Use Generic sheet 6 for word wheels with the digraph as the initial phoneme. Write this in the centre of the wheel and ask the children to complete words by writing them out towards the rim of the wheel.

ch

I love chips and cheese!

Write

◆Charlie the chimp swings from a chain.

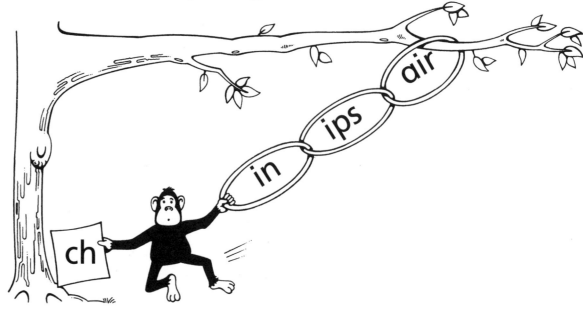

◆Join ch to the other letters to make ch words. Write them here.

ch_____    ch_____

ch_____

Choose a ch word. Draw a picture of it.

◆ Charlie the chimp swings from a chain.

◆ Join **ch** to the other letters to make four **ch** words.

_____    _____

_____    _____

Write two new **ch** words.
Draw a picture of them.

◆ Choose one word and draw it.

ch

Write ch.

I love chips and cheese! Zep

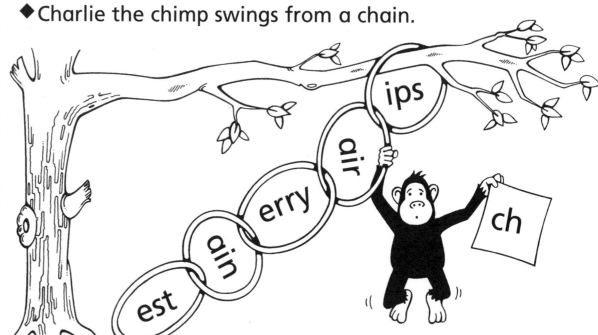

◆Charlie the chimp swings from a chain.

◆Join ch to the other letters to make five ch words.

_____  _____  _____

_____  _____

◆Choose one word and draw it.

◆Write three new ch words.

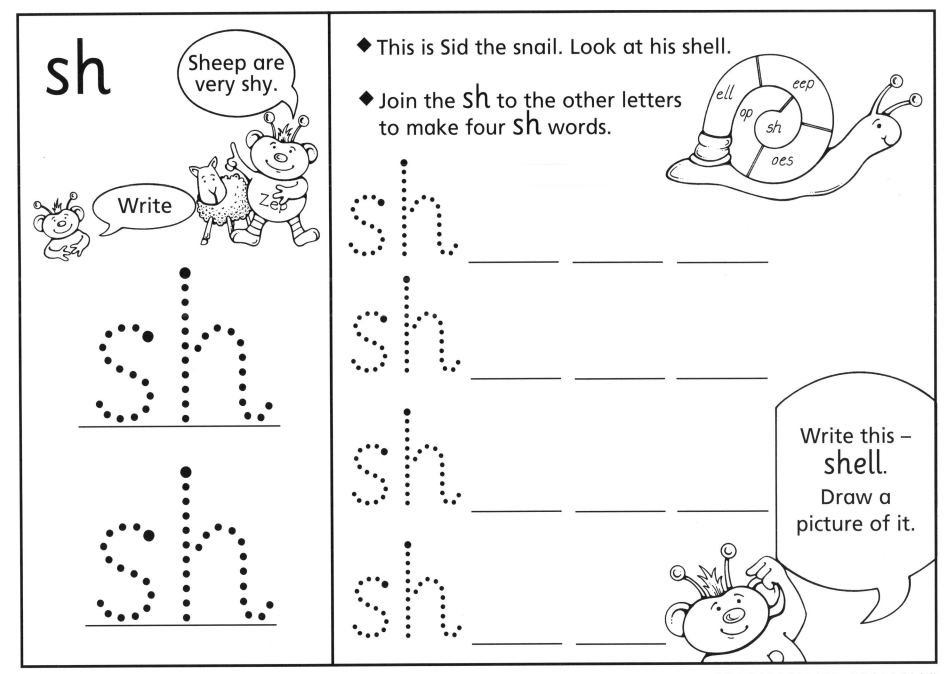

**sh**

Sheep are very shy.

Write

This is Sid the snail. Look at his shell.

Join the sh to the other letters to make four sh words.

ell    eep    op    sh    oes

Write this – **shell**. Draw a picture of it.

sh    _____ _____ _____

sh    _____ _____ _____

sh    _____ _____ _____

sh    _____ _____ _____

PHONICABILITY RECEPTION

sh

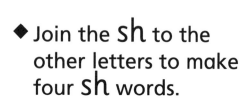

**sh**  sh.

sh.

◆ This is Sid the snail. Look at his shell.

◆ Join the **sh** to the other letters to make four **sh** words.

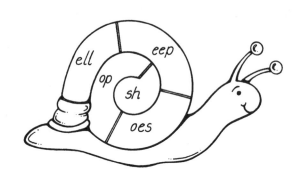

_____

_____

_____

_____

Write two new **sh** words. Draw pictures of them.

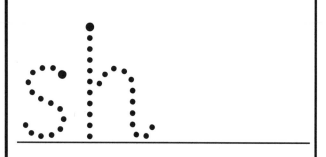

# sh

Sheep are very shy.

Write sh.

Zep

◆ This is Sid the snail. Look at his shell.

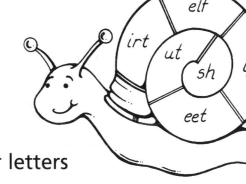

elf
irt
ut
sh
ip
eet

◆ Join the sh to the other letters to make five sh words.

Write three new sh words. Draw pictures of them.

# th

This is my thumb.

Write

◆ This is Theo the thrush. Look at his eggs.

in    umb    ree

th

◆ Join **th** to the letters in the eggs to make three **th** words.

_____    _____    _____

◆ Draw a thistle.

Write this –
**thumb**.
Draw a picture of it.

## th

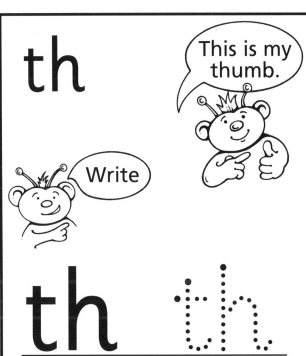

This is my thumb.

Write

## th

th

th

◆ This is Theo the thrush. Look at his eggs.

ink  umb  istle  ree

th

◆ Join **th** to the letters in the eggs to make four **th** words.

_____  _____

_____  _____

◆ Draw three thistles.

Write a new **th** word. Draw a picture of it.

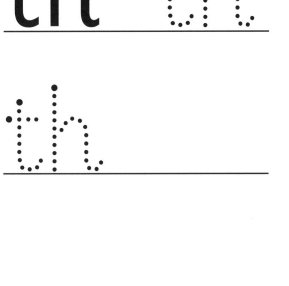

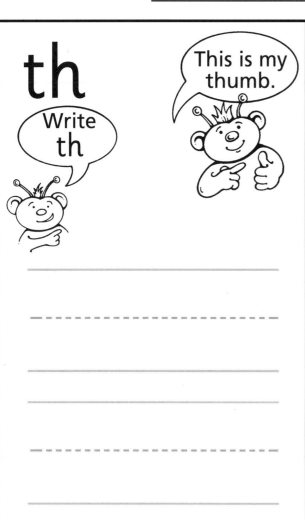

th

Write th

This is my thumb.

◆ This is Theo the thrush. Look at his eggs.

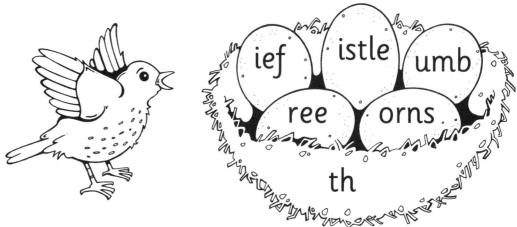

ief   istle   umb   ree   orns   th

◆ Join **th** to the letters in the eggs to make five **th** words.

_____   _____

_____   _____

_____

◆ Draw Theo the thrush on a thistle.

Write more **th** words. Draw pictures of them.

◆ Draw a line from each picture to its beginning sound.

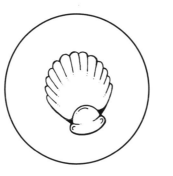

| ch | sh | th |

◆ Draw things that begin with ch, sh and th.

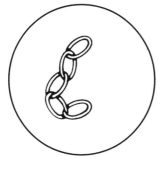

◆ Write the beginning sound for each picture.

_ _ oes

_ _ ief

_ _ ree

_ _ icken

| ch | sh | th |
|----|----|----|

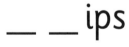
_ _ ips

◆ Write new ch, sh and th words.

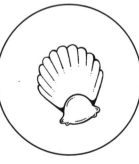
_ _ ell

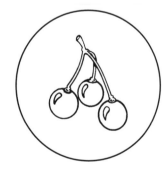
_ _ erries

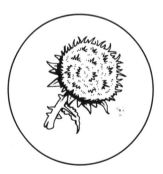
_ _ istle

_ _ op

◆ Write the words.    <u>ch</u>    <u>sh</u>    <u>th</u>

_____    _____    _____

_____

◆ Write more things that begin with **ch**, **sh** or **th**.

    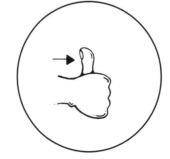        

_____    _____    _____    _____

# Phonicability

## SECTION 3

## Onset, rime and c-v-c

# Onset, rime and c-v-c

## OVERALL AIMS

○ To learn the definitions of 'onset' and 'rime'.
○ To be able to listen to, identify and write the onset or rime in words.
○ To be able to discriminate initial, medial and final phonemes in consonant-vowel-consonant (c-v-c) words.
○ To be able to listen to, identify and write any phoneme of a c-v-c word.
○ To be able to build up c-v-c words independently.

## TEACHER'S NOTES

It is vital that children develop the ability to discriminate the individual phonemes within words. This skill forms the basis of successful reading, spelling and writing. The child needs to be able to sound out the words and know how they are built up. This will develop their awareness of the construction of words in particular and language in general.

An excellent strategy to develop the ability to differentiate between onset and rime is to use rhyming and poetry, together with chants to illustrate the required sounds. For example, 'men', 'pen', 'hen' and 'den' all have the same rime – it is the onset that differs; 'clap', 'clang' and 'clatter' all have the same onset – it is the rime that differs.

Children enjoy using technical terms and need to familiarise themselves with those that are constantly referred to throughout the *National Literacy Framework*. It is important that they become confident in using these terms correctly and in an appropriate context. 'Onset' and 'rime' are terms that they need to become familiar with in their early phonics sessions.

## INTENDED LEARNING

○ To differentiate between the onset or the rime of a given c-v-c word.
○ To know what the terms 'onset' and 'rime' mean and begin to use them appropriately.
○ To identify the medial phoneme of a c-v-c word.
○ To be able to build up a c-v-c word from given phonemes.

## SUGGESTED ACTIVITIES

### Onset and rime

○ Choose a c-v-c word that can be rhymed with several others. For example, 'hat' can be rhymed with 'mat', 'bat', 'cat', 'fat', 'pat', 'rat' and 'sat'. Ask the children "What's the same about all these words?" Give another word that can be rhymed, such as 'pen' and ask the children for words that rhyme with it. Explain that this similar ending is called the rime. Ensure they know the difference between 'rime' and 'rhyme'. (Two rimes don't necessarily rhyme!)
○ Sing some well known nursery rhymes with the children. Ask them to identify the words in each rhyme with the same rime. Differentiate between the rime and the onset of these words.
○ Look at a nursery rhyme book. Pick out the rhyming words in three nursery rhymes. Write the rime on yellow paper and the onset on white paper. Stick the two parts onto black paper to display the whole word. Challenge the children to find more words to add to the display.
○ Make a collection of items with the same rime. Make a display on a side table, for example a cat, a mat, a bat and a hat. If there is no room for the real

objects, use models or pictures. Write labels to identify each displayed object, using different colours to highlight the onset and the rime. Ask the children to match the labels to the objects. Challenge them to find other objects to add to the collection.
○ Ask the children to draw four things that have the same rime. Ask them to write the names of the objects.
○ Make word wheels where the children match onset and rimes to make words. (Use the template sheet on page 126 in the generic sheets section at the back of this book.)
○ Work as a whole class to change the words in well known nursery rhymes to make new rhymes. For example:

> To market, to market
> To buy a fat <u>hen</u>
> Home again, home again
> Jiggerty, <u>jen</u>

○ Write simple poems where the children provide the endings, for example:

> As wet as a fish, as dry as a bone
> As live as a fish, as dead as a _____

○ Draw some large animal shapes. Write suitable captions for each one, for example 'I am a dog and I only say...' (hog, fog, log, bog). Discuss with the children the words that could go with each picture and write them inside the animal shape. Challenge them to add to the lists over time.
○ Ask the children to bring in greetings cards. Talk about the rhymes used in the messages inside. They could make their own cards and write a rhyming message.

### C-v-c words

○ Write the vowels on the board. Tell the children that these are called vowels and that one of them is often the middle phoneme of a word with three phonemes. Write some examples of c-v-c words on the board. Ask "What's the middle phoneme of this word?" Ask the children if they can think if some c-v-c words themselves. If they can, let them write the words on the board themselves. Ask each child "What's the middle phoneme of your word?" or ask the class, "What's the middle phoneme of David's word?"

○ Enlarge one page of a magazine or newspaper and ask the children to cut out all the c-v-c words they can find. Glue the words onto cards. Ask the children to work in pairs to make up sentences using the words.

○ Make five columns on a large sheet of paper or a flip-chart. Head them with the vowels. Ask the children to come and write a c-v-c word in one of the columns, ensuring that the word is in the correct column for its medial phoneme.

○ Ask the children to draw pictures of c-v-c objects, for example a hat, dog, man, net, pan and so on. Put the drawings into a class book with the words or captions underneath each picture. Put the book in the reading corner for the children to share.

○ Ask the children to look in a simple dictionary for c-v-c words. Ask them to make a display of those words with plastic letters on a tray.

○ Make a display of objects that are c-v-c words. Label the objects. Challenge the children to find other objects to add to the display.

### USING THE DIFFERENTIATED ACTIVITY SHEETS

Read the instructions on each sheet to the groups.

#### Activity sheets a
These sheets are intended to give practice in identifying the onset, rime and medial phoneme of c-v-c words, saying them and writing them independently. They are for children who still need to consolidate the skill of breaking up a c-v-c word into its three phonemic components.

#### Activity sheets b
These sheets are intended to give practice in identifying the onset, rime and medial phoneme of c-v-c words. They also encourage the child to develop the ability to write c-v-c words independently, but with a little support.

#### Activity sheets c
These sheets are intended to give practice in identifying the onset, rime and medial phoneme of c-v-c words. They also encourage the child to develop the ability to write c-v-c words independently within sentences, with the minimum of support.

The mixed activity sheets give further practice and reinforcement of these skills.

### GENERIC SHEETS

○ Use Generic sheet 1 to practise letter formation or sentence writing.

○ Use Generic sheet 2 to make a cube or a dice. Write one vowel on each face. The children take turns to roll it and name the vowel. They then write a c-v-c- word with that vowel as the medial phoneme.

○ Use Generic sheet 3 to make a word wheel. Cut out the circles and pin the smaller to the larger using a split pin through the centre. How many c-v-c words can the children make?

○ Use Generic sheet 4 to make c-v-c cards for Snap or Pelmanism games. Stick the sheet onto card before cutting out the boxes. Write a c-v-c word on each pair of cards.

○ Use Generic sheet 4 to make c-v-c dominoes. Stick the sheet onto card before cutting out the boxes. Draw a line down the centre of each box and write a c-v-c word on each half.

○ Use Generic sheet 5 for wordsearches or crosswords. Activity sheets for phonemes 'c' and 's' illustrate these.

○ Use Generic sheet 6 for word wheels. Place the onset phoneme at the centre of the wheel and ask the children to complete c-v-c words by writing them out towards the rim of the wheel.

○ Use Generic sheet 7 to make c-v-c word tracks. The final phoneme of one word forms the initial phoneme of the next.

◆ Draw a line from each picture to its beginning sound.

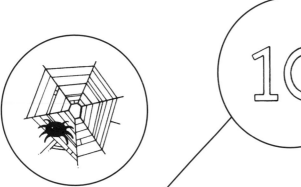

| t | d | w | c | j | s | h |

◆ Say the sounds.
◆ Write some of them on the lines here.

_____    _____    _____

_____    _____    _____

◆ Write the sound at the beginning of the words.

\_ at

\_ ap

\_ ox

\_ ip

| b | p | c | m | z | t |
|---|---|---|---|---|---|

\_ an

\_ an

Say the sounds you have written.
Write the words again.

◆ Write the word under each picture.

  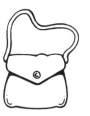      

_____    _____    _____    _____    _____

◆ Write the beginning sounds in this box.

_____    _____

◆ Write a sentence for two of the words.

_____

_____

Draw pictures of things that begin with n, g and l. Write the words.

◆ Draw a line from each picture to its final sound.

b   n   x   g   t   p   s

◆ Say the final sounds.
◆ Write some of them on the lines here.

_____   _____   _____

_____   _____   _____

◆ Write the final sounds. Then write out each word again.

bu__

____

ju__

____

ma__

____

si__

____

| x | n | t | s | p | g |

cu__

____

te__

____

Say the final sounds you have written.
Say the words you have written.

◆ Write the word under each picture.

     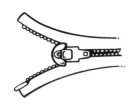               

_____     _____     _____     _____     _____

          ◆ Write the final sound of each word in this box.

_____     _____

◆ Write a sentence using two of the words.

_____

◆ Write new words that end in t, n and g.
◆ Draw pictures of them.

◆ Follow the arrows to make the words. Write the words.

| a | e | i | o | u |
|---|---|---|---|---|

c

a
t

p
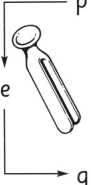
e
g

z
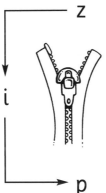
i
p

d

o
g

c
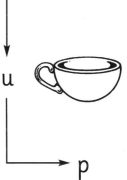
u
p

_____   _____   _____   _____   _____

◆ Write the middle sound.

m _ p     l _ g     t _ n

h _ t     s _ t

Write two more words.
Draw pictures of them.

113

◆ Write the words.

a  e  i  o  u

   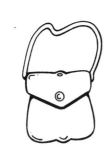         

m_ _        b_ _        h_ _        t_ _        j_ _

◆ Write the middle sound.

b _ x          p _ n

z _ p          t _ n

c _ t          s _ t

h _ t          m _ g

Write three more
words.
Draw pictures of
them.

114

◆ Sort out the mixed-up letters and write the words.

ath          jgu          toc          int          dbe

____         ____         ____         ____         ____

◆ Now do these.

xbo          tac          anp

____         ____         ____

elg          piz          uns

____         ____         ____

Choose two words and write sentences about them. Draw pictures.

Name _____    Date _____

◆ **Choose the right sounds. Write them under the pictures.**

| m b j |  | f g t |  | o e u |  |

\_ed    ca\_    h\_n

| g p d | | u a o | | m p d | |

\_og    b\_x    \_eg

◆ Say the sounds you have written.

◆ Say the words you have written.

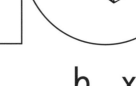

116

◆ Choose the right sounds. Write them under the pictures.

o u e i a

j_g

e c s z o

bu__

n u h m w

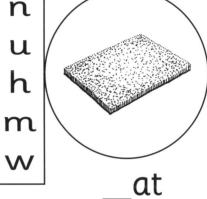

__at

f t h g j

__ap

l t i j k

t_n

u m n h p

pa__

◆ Say the sounds you have written.

◆ Write a sentence about one of the words.

◆ **Choose the right sounds. Write them under the pictures.**

| d | s |
|---|---|
| p | z |
| b | x |
| g | y |
| q | w |

_ o _

| o | d |
|---|---|
| u | p |
| i | q |
| e | g |
| a | b |

w_ _

_ _ g

| g | a |
|---|---|
| h | e |
| j | i |
| t | o |
| f | u |

| a | f |
|---|---|
| e | g |
| i | t |
| o | h |
| u | j |

r_ _

| b | o |
|---|---|
| q | u |
| d | a |
| p | i |
| g | e |

_ _ g

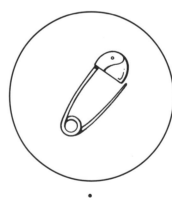

_ i _

| p | m |
|---|---|
| b | u |
| d | w |
| g | n |
| q | a |

◆Say the sounds you have written.          ◆Write a sentence for four of the words.

118

# Phonicability

## SECTION 4

### Generic Sheets

# Using the generic sheets

### GENERIC SHEET 1

This sheet provides blank tracks for practising letter formation, or guided sentence writing. It enables the children to see the relative positioning and shape of letters. It is useful at the early stages of learning letters and letter shape.

### GENERIC SHEET 2

Many phonics activities and games include the use of a cube or dice. This sheet provides a template for both. A new dice can be made for each phonics rule and the required phonemes can be written on the faces.

### GENERIC SHEET 3

This is a format for a word wheel game for c-v-c words. It can be adapted by blanking out the given letters and clusters and replacing them with those required by the teacher.

### GENERIC SHEET 4

This sheet provides the master for making Snap cards, Pelmanism cards or label cards.

### GENERIC SHEET 5

The use of this sheet enables you to make your own word searches or crosswords. They can be used to make puzzles relevant to the particular phonics rule being taught.

### GENERIC SHEET 6

This blank word wheel can be used for puzzles and games relevant to the phonics rule being taught.

### GENERIC SHEET 7

This train track can be used to make games for single phonemes, digraphs or c-v-c words as required. For example, various three-letter words can be written on the track and the children have to colour the words beginning with 'c', or those with the medial vowel 'e', or those ending with 't'. Another idea is to write the beginning of a pattern in the tracks, such as c, f, c, f or ch, th, sh, ch, th, sh and the children have to complete the pattern. For those still working with initial sounds, various letters could be written on the track and the children asked colour in every occurrence of a specified letter, such as 'c'.

Name _____  Date _____

122

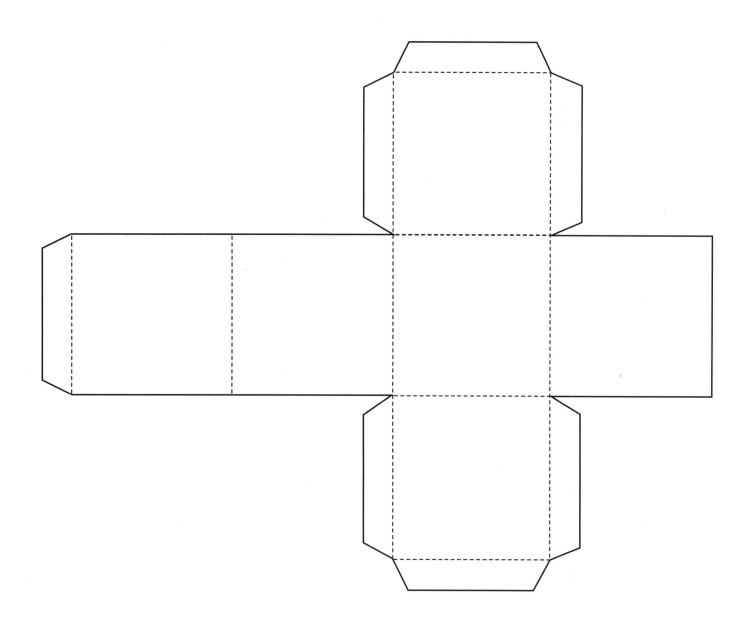

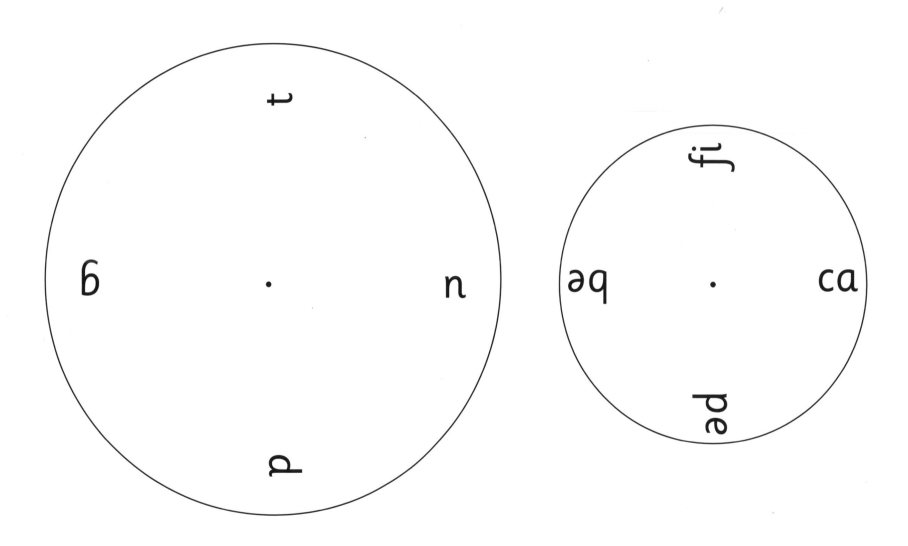

# Generic sheet 4

# Generic sheet 5

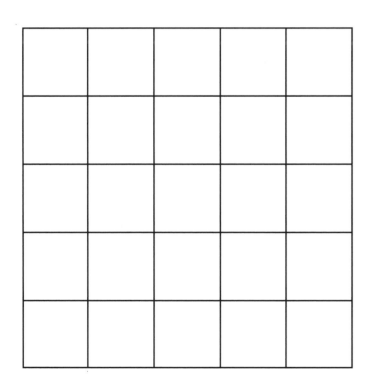

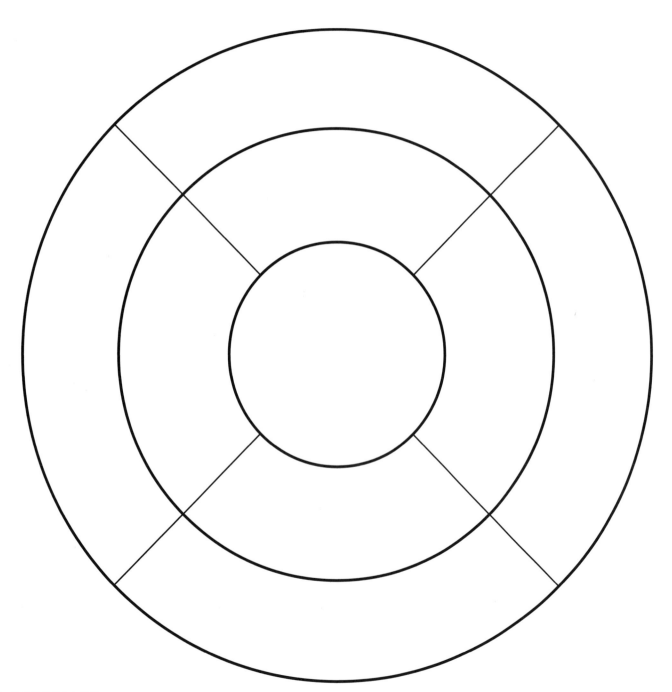

Name _____  Date _____

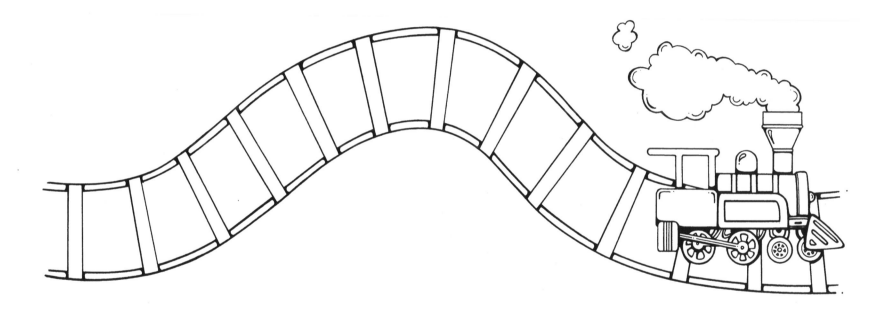

# Phonics Record/Assessment Sheet

Name

Year                    Level                                    Date

| TARGET SKILL | | NLSF REFERENCE |
|---|---|---|
| **(Step 2)** | | YR |
| **1** Can continue a rhyming string | | 1a |
| **2** Can hear & say phonemes s/m/k/t/g/h in  initial position | | 2a, 2b |
| **3** Knows phoneme-grapheme correspondences s/m/c/t/g/h | | 2d, 4c |
| **(Step 3** | | YR |
| **1** Can hear & say phonemes in the final position | | 1b, 1c |
| **2** Knows phoneme-grapheme correspondences l/n/d/k/sh/ch | | 2e |
| **(Step 4)** | | YR |
| **1** Can hear & say phonemes in the medial position a/e/i/o/u | | 2b, 2c |
| **2** Knows phoneme-grapheme correspondences a/e/i/o/u/f/q/b/r/j/p/th | | 2e, 4c |
| **3** Can segment and spell c-v-c words | | Y1 |
| **4** Can blend to read c-v-c words | | Term 1: 4, 5, 6 |
| **(Step 5)** | | |
| **1** Can hear phonemes within consonant clusters ch/sh/th | | |
| **2** Knows phoneme-grapheme correspondences v/w/x/y/z | | YR |
| **3** Can segment and spell c-c-v-c words (ch-v-c/ sh-v-c/ th-v-c)& c-v-c-c words ( c-v-ch/ c-v-sh/ c-v-th) | | 2b, 2c |
| **4** Can blend to read c-c-v-c words & c-v-c-c words | | |

**Relevant Comments:**